Supernatural S...
Shakespeare'...

First Witch

Second Witch

Third Witch

Macbeth

Banquo

Ross

Angus

Hecate

First Apparition

Second Apparition

Third Apparition

Introducing the story of Macbeth ...

At the start of the play, Macbeth is a
brave soldier. He has just been fighting a
battle in support of King Duncan of Scotland.

The story ...

The three witches plan to meet Macbeth after the battle. They have magical powers. They are ruled by other spirits.

What might the characters be thinking ...?

"When shall we meet? What shall we do? How can we make trouble for Macbeth?"

Useful words ...

hurlyburly confusion

ere before

heath a common, or open land

graymalkin, Paddock
the witches' animals (usually a cat and a toad)

anon I'm coming now

An open place.

Thunder and lightning. Enter three Witches

FIRST WITCH   When shall we three meet again
              In thunder, lightning, or in rain?

SECOND WITCH When the hurlyburly's done,
              When the battle's lost and won.

THIRD WITCH   That will be ere the set of sun.

FIRST WITCH   Where the place?

SECOND WITCH Upon the heath.

THIRD WITCH   There to meet with Macbeth.

FIRST WITCH   I come, Graymalkin!

SECOND WITCH Paddock calls.

THIRD WITCH   Anon.

ALL   Fair is foul, and foul is fair:
              Hover through the fog and filthy air.

Exeunt

3

The story ...

The three witches meet again. The second witch has been killing pigs. The first witch is angry with a sailor's wife who wouldn't share some chestnuts with her. The witch plans to make trouble for the sailor who is at sea in a ship called *The Tiger*.

What might the characters be thinking ...?

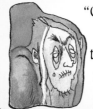

"Quite a good day's work making trouble! Now let's make trouble for that sailor!"

Useful words ...

thou/thee you (**thou art** you are)

swine pigs

quoth said

aroint go away

rump-fed ronyon a rude name for a woman

Aleppo a town in Syria

thither to there

A heath near Forres.

Thunder. Enter the three Witches

FIRST WITCH   Where hast thou been, sister?

SECOND WITCH Killing swine.

THIRD WITCH   Sister, where thou?

FIRST WITCH   A sailor's wife had chestnuts in her lap,
And munch'd, and munch'd, and munch'd:
'Give me,' quoth I:
'Aroint thee, witch!' the rump-fed ronyon cries.
Her husband's to Aleppo gone, master o' the Tiger:
But in a sieve I'll thither sail,
And, like a rat without a tail,
I'll do, I'll do, and I'll do.

SECOND WITCH I'll give thee a wind.

FIRST WITCH   Thou'rt kind.

THIRD WITCH   And I another.

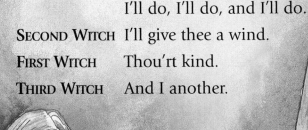

The story ...

The first witch decides on a curse to put on the sailor. The witches know that Macbeth is just about to appear.

What might the characters be thinking ...?

"We'll control all the winds between us. That sailor won't get any sleep for weeks and weeks. Even if the ship isn't wrecked we'll make sure it's in some terrible storms!"

Useful words ...

penthouse lid eyelids

bark ship

tempest-tost thrown about by storms

FIRST WITCH I myself have all the other …
… I will drain him dry as hay:
Sleep shall neither night nor day
Hang upon his penthouse lid;
He shall live a man forbid …
… Though his bark cannot be lost,
Yet it shall be tempest-tost.

Look what I have.

SECOND WITCH Show me, show me.

FIRST WITCH Here I have a pilot's thumb,
Wreck'd as homeward he did come.

Drum within

THIRD WITCH A drum, a drum!
Macbeth doth come.

7

The story ...

Macbeth and his friend Banquo meet the three witches for the first time. They are shocked by the witches' strange looks.

What might the characters be thinking ...?

"We'll work together to make this spell for Macbeth a powerful one!"

"This is a very strange day ... What on earth...! Can they speak?"

"Are these humans? Are they women? They look wild!"

Useful words ...

posters travellers

thrice three times

chappy chapped, rough

forbid me to interpret make it impossible for me to think

ALL   The weird sisters, hand in hand,
             Posters of the sea and land,
             Thus do go about, about:
             Thrice to thine, and thrice to mine,
             And thrice again, to make up nine.
             Peace! the charm's wound up.

Enter Macbeth and Banquo

MACBETH   So foul and fair a day I have not seen.

BANQUO   … What are these
             So wither'd and so wild in their attire,
             That look not like the inhabitants o' the earth,
             And yet are on't? Live you? Or are you aught
             That man may question? You seem to understand me,
             By each at once her chappy finger laying
             Upon her skinny lips: you should be women,
             And yet your beards forbid me to interpret
             That you are so.

MACBETH   Speak, if you can: what are you?

9

The story ...

The witches call Macbeth Thane of Glamis (a title he already has), Thane of Cawdor (which he is not), and future King of Scotland. Macbeth does not speak at first. Banquo is surprised by his friend's reaction. Banquo asks about his own future.

What might the characters be thinking ...?

"What! Can they read my mind? I must act normally or Banquo will suspect something."

"Why does Macbeth seem so shocked? It's not bad news to hear you might be King! I'd like to know what they think is going to happen to me – I think I'll ask them."

Useful words ...

hereafter after this

start jump with surprise

fantastical imaginary

seeds of time the future

FIRST WITCH	All hail, Macbeth! hail to thee, Thane of Glamis!
SECOND WITCH	All hail, Macbeth, hail to thee, Thane of Cawdor!
THIRD WITCH	All hail, Macbeth, thou shalt be King hereafter!
BANQUO	Good sir, why do you start; and seem to fear
	Things that do sound so fair? I' the name of truth,
	Are ye fantastical …?

                       … My noble partner
You greet with present grace and great prediction
Of noble having and of royal hope …
… to me you speak not.
If you can look into the seeds of time,
And say which grain will grow and which will not,
Speak then to me, who neither beg nor fear
Your favours nor your hate.

The story ...

The witches predict that Banquo's family will become kings. When Macbeth sees the witches are about to disappear, he calls for them to stay.

What might the characters be thinking ...?

"Banquo's family becoming kings! I thought I'm the one who's going to be King!"

"What can this mean?"

Useful words ...

get be the father of

FIRST WITCH	Hail!
SECOND WITCH	Hail!
THIRD WITCH	Hail!
FIRST WITCH	Lesser than Macbeth, and greater.
SECOND WITCH	Not so happy, yet much happier.
THIRD WITCH	Thou shalt get kings, though thou be none: So all hail, Macbeth and Banquo!
FIRST WITCH	Banquo and Macbeth, all hail!
MACBETH	Stay, you imperfect speakers, tell me more …

Witches vanish

The story ...

Banquo and Macbeth talk about what the witches have said. Two messengers arrive from the King. The King is very pleased with the way Macbeth fought in the battles.

What might the characters be thinking ...?

"They seemed real but they just melted into thin air! This is really exciting. What do these messengers want? Well, I'm glad that the King has been hearing such good things about me."

"They disappeared like bubbles in the air! Have we taken a drug that's making us see these strange sights? Macbeth seems very excited. What do these messengers want?"

"It's good to be bringing some good news. Macbeth is a great soldier."

Useful words ...

whither where (or where to)

would if only

takes the reason prisoner a root that makes you go mad

selfsame exactly the same

thy your

bear carry

BANQUO   The earth hath bubbles, as the water has,
          And these are of them. Whither are they vanish'd?

MACBETH   Into the air … melted
          As breath into the wind. Would they had stay'd!

BANQUO   Were such things here as we do speak about?
          Or have we eaten on the insane root
          That takes the reason prisoner?

MACBETH   Your children shall be kings.

BANQUO   You shall be King.

MACBETH   And Thane of Cawdor too: went it not so?

BANQUO   To the selfsame tune and words. Who's here?

Enter Ross and Angus

ROSS   The king hath happily received, Macbeth,
          The news of thy success …

                              … As thick as hail
          Came post with post; and every one did bear
          Thy praises in his kingdom's great defence,
          And pour'd them down before him.

15

The story ...

Ross and Angus tell Macbeth that the King has decided to make him Thane of Cawdor.

What might the characters be thinking ...?

"Thane of Cawdor! So ... two out of three predictions have already come true – only one more to go ..."

"I can't believe this is happening! There's something evil about all of this."

"Why do they both look so shocked?"

Useful words ...

bade told

thine yours

ANGUS	We are sent To give thee from our royal master thanks …
ROSS	And … he bade me, from him, call thee Thane of Cawdor: … Hail, most worthy Thane! For it is thine.
BANQUO	What, can the devil speak true …?
MACBETH	*(Aside)* Glamis, and Thane of Cawdor! The greatest is behind.

The story ...

Time has passed and Macbeth has become an evil man. He has
murdered King Duncan with a dagger while he was asleep and a
guest at Macbeth's castle. Macbeth then became King of
Scotland, as the witches had predicted. Only Lady Macbeth
(Macbeth's wife) knows the secret of Duncan's murder, although
other people are suspicious.

King Duncan's sons have fled to England where they are
gathering an army to fight against Macbeth. Macduff, a powerful
man and a soldier, becomes suspicious of Macbeth and leaves to
join the army against Macbeth.

Macbeth cannot stop thinking about the witches' predictions.
He wants to stop Banquo's family becoming kings. Even though
Banquo is his friend, Macbeth arranges to have him and his son
murdered while they are out riding. The murderers kill Banquo
but his son manages to escape, so in Macbeth's mind the
witches' predictions for Banquo's family can still come true.

Both Macbeth and Lady Macbeth are becoming more and more
troubled by the evil they have done. At a large public feast,
Macbeth believes he can see the ghost of Banquo. No one else
can see the ghost. Macbeth's behaviour is becoming suspicious
and he has few friends. He decides to go to find the witches
again, in the hope that they will set his mind at rest. At the
beginning of Act IV we see the witches making a magic spell.

A cavern. In the middle, a boiling cauldron.

Thunder. Enter the three Witches

FIRST WITCH	Thrice the brinded cat hath mew'd.
SECOND WITCH	Thrice and once the hedge-pig whined.
THIRD WITCH	Harpier cries; 'Tis time, 'tis time.
FIRST WITCH	Round about the cauldron go;
	In the poison'd entrails throw.
	Toad, that under cold stone
	Days and nights has thirty-one
	Swelter'd venom sleeping got,
	Boil thou first i' the charmed pot.
ALL	Double, double toil and trouble;
	Fire burn, and cauldron bubble.

Useful words ...

brinded striped

hedge-pig hedgehog

Harpier a witch's animal

cauldron large pot

entrails guts

swelter'd venom, sleeping got poison sweated out during sleep

What might the characters be thinking ...?

"Let's make something really nasty before Macbeth arrives ..."

The story ...

The witches continue to boil up their magic spell.

What might the characters be thinking ...?

"Let's put in some really horrible things ..."

Useful words ...

fillet strip of meat

fenny from the fens or marshland

adder's fork adder's forked tongue

owlet young owl

maw mouth

ravin'd full (from having eaten its prey)

hemlock poisonous plant

gruel thin soup

slab slimy

chaudron guts

SECOND WITCH Fillet of a fenny snake,
In the cauldron boil and bake;
Eye of newt and toe of frog,
Wool of bat and tongue of dog,
Adder's fork and blind-worm's sting,
Lizard's leg and owlet's wing,
For a charm of powerful trouble,
Like a hell-broth boil and bubble.

ALL Double, double toil and trouble;
Fire burn and cauldron bubble.

THIRD WITCH Scale of dragon, tooth of wolf,
Witches' mummy, maw and gulf
Of the ravin'd salt-sea shark,
Root of hemlock digg'd i' the dark …
… Finger of birth-strangled babe …
Make the gruel thick and slab:
Add thereto a tiger's chaudron,
For the ingredients of our cauldron.

ALL Double, double toil and trouble;
Fire burn and cauldron bubble.

SECOND WITCH Cool it with a baboon's blood,
Then the charm is firm and good.

21

The story ...

Hecate, the witches' mistress, likes the spell they have been making in their cauldron. Macbeth arrives.

What might the characters be thinking ...?

"Good! This will work well."

"They're here! But what are they doing?"

Useful words ...

commend praise

hags witches

Enter Hecate (to the other three Witches)

HECATE O well done! I commend your pains;
And every one shall share i' the gains;
And now about the cauldron sing,
Like elves and fairies in a ring,
Enchanting all that you put in.

MUSIC AND Black spirits and white, red spirits and gray;
A SONG Mingle, mingle, mingle, you that mingle may.

Exit Hecate

SECOND WITCH By the pricking of my thumbs,
Something wicked this way comes.
Open, locks, whoever knocks!

Enter Macbeth

MACBETH How now, you secret, black, and midnight hags!
What is't you do?

ALL A deed without a name.

The story ...

Macbeth begs the witches to answer his questions. The witches will let him hear the answers from their own masters.

What might the characters be thinking ...?

"They *must* answer my questions. I'll beg them."

"He doesn't know what he's in for! Let's call up the masters!"

Useful words ...

conjure call upon

yesty foaming

confound and swallow navigation upset and swallow ships

MACBETH I conjure you …
Howe'er you come to know it, answer me:
Though you untie the winds and let them fight
Against the churches; though the yesty waves
Confound and swallow navigation up;
Though bladed corn be lodged and trees blown down;
Though castles topple on their warders' heads;
Though palaces and pyramids do slope
Their heads to their foundations; … answer me
To what I ask you.

FIRST WITCH Speak.

SECOND WITCH Demand.

THIRD WITCH We'll answer.

FIRST WITCH Say, if thou'dst rather hear it from our mouths,
Or from our masters?

MACBETH Call 'em; let me see 'em.

The story ...

The witches conjure up the First Apparition, a head wearing armour, who warns Macbeth to beware of Macduff.

What might the characters be thinking ...?

"It'll begin with something he'll find it easy to believe ..."

"Yes, Macduff! Just as I feared. Now I need to find out more ... but it's gone!"

Useful words ...

farrow piglets

gibbet gallows (used to hang people)

deftly quickly

apparition ghost

harp'd guessed

potent powerful

FIRST WITCH:	Pour in sow's blood, that hath eaten Her nine farrow; grease that's sweaten From the murderer's gibbet throw Into the flame.
ALL	Come, high or low; Thyself and office deftly show!

Thunder. First Apparition: an Armed Head

MACBETH	Tell me, thou unknown power –
FIRST WITCH	He knows thy thought: Hear his speech, but say thou nought.
FIRST APPARITION	Macbeth! Macbeth! Macbeth! beware Macduff; Beware the Thane of Fife. Dismiss me. Enough.

Descends

MACBETH	Whate'er thou art, for thy good caution, thanks; Thou hast harp'd my fear aright: but one word more –
FIRST WITCH	He will not be commanded: here's another, More potent than the first.

The story ...

The Second Apparition, a bloody child,
appears and tells Macbeth he cannot be
harmed by a man born of a woman. The
Third and most powerful Apparition appears:
a child wearing a crown and holding a tree.

What might the characters be thinking ...?

"Then Macduff can't
hurt me – I don't need
to be afraid of him ...
But that doesn't fit with
what the First
Apparition said ..."

Useful words ...

resolute determined

make assurance double sure make doubly sure

bond promise

issue the descendants (children) of a person

round and top of sovereignty crown

Thunder. Second Apparition: A Bloody Child

SECOND APPARITION	Macbeth! Macbeth! Macbeth!
MACBETH	Had I three ears, I'd hear thee.
SECOND APPARITION	Be bloody, bold, and resolute; laugh to scorn The power of man, for none of woman born Shall harm Macbeth.

Descends

MACBETH   Then live, Macduff: what need I fear of thee?
But yet I'll make assurance double sure,
And take a bond of fate: thou shalt not live;
That I may tell pale-hearted fear it lies,
And sleep in spite of thunder.

Thunder. Third Apparition: a Child crowned, with a tree in his hand

What is this
That rises like the issue of a king,
And wears upon his baby-brow the round
And top of sovereignty?

ALL   Listen, but speak not to't.

The story ....

The Third Apparition tells Macbeth that he won't be beaten until Birnam Wood moves to Dunsinane Hill. Macbeth believes this could never happen and that he will be safe. The spirits start to disappear, but Macbeth wants to hear if Banquo's family will become kings. He demands that the spirits stay. The witches prepare to show him something that he will not like …

What might the characters be thinking …?

"Birnam Wood to Dunsinane Hill! Impossible! Then I am safe. But I must know about Banquo's family …Curse them! They must tell me!"

"He will not like this … what a pleasant night's work!"

Useful words ...

lion-mettled with the courage of a lion

chafes … frets irritates

conspirers people who make plots

vanquish'd beaten

bodements predictions

issue the descendants (children) of a person

grieve his heart make his heart break with sorrow

THIRD APPARITION	Be lion-mettled, proud; and take no care Who chafes, who frets, or where conspirers are: Macbeth shall never vanquish'd be until Great Birnam Wood to high Dunsinane Hill Shall come against him.
Descends	
MACBETH	That will never be Who can impress the forest, bid the tree Unfix his earth-bound root? Sweet bodements! good! … Yet my heart Throbs to know one thing: tell me, if your art Can tell so much: shall Banquo's issue ever Reign in this kingdom?
ALL	Seek to know no more.
MACBETH	I will be satisfied: deny me this, And an eternal curse fall on you! Let me know. Why sinks that cauldron? and what noise is this?
FIRST WITCH	Show!
SECOND WITCH	Show!
THIRD WITCH	Show!
ALL	Show his eyes, and grieve his heart; Come like shadows, so depart!

31

The end of the story

Lady Macbeth dies a miserable death, filled with guilt and unable to find peace. Macbeth prepares for the battle against the army from England at Dunsinane Hill. He seems to believe still in the witches' predictions, but he is badly shaken by the fact that the soldiers have stripped branches from the trees in Birnam Wood to use as camouflage. Birnam Wood has, in a sense, come to Dunsinane.

But Macbeth fights bravely, and kills many enemy soldiers. Finally he comes up against Macduff. He taunts Macduff, saying that no one born of woman can kill him. Macduff reveals that he was born by a Caesarean operation, which means that he was taken from his mother's womb rather than being born in the usual way. The witches' predictions have been both true and false. Macbeth realises that he has been deceived. Macduff kills Macbeth. King Duncan's sons can now take the throne of Scotland – and Banquo's family can become kings in the future.